LITTLE HE

LUV KUSH

Little Heroes

LUV KUSH

Published by:

Mind Melodies

An imprint of ***Readworthy Publications (P) Ltd.***

A-18, Mohan Garden, Near Nawada Metro Station, New Delhi – 110 059

Phone: (011) 2537 1324 Fax: +91-11-2537 1323

www.mindmelodies.com

Email: info@mindmelodies.com

ISBN-10 81-89973-11-8

ISBN-13 978-81-89973-11-7

EAN 9788189973117

Long ago, when Lord Rama's wife, Sita, was banished from Ayodhya, she sought shelter in Sage Valmiki's hermitage in the forest, along the river, Ganga. "My child! Do not worry at all. Consider this hermitage as your paternal home. You will certainly rejoin Rama one day," said Valmiki. And so, Sita became the guest of Sage Valmiki.

After sometime, Sita gave birth to her twin sons—Luv and Kush. The children knew that they were living in Lord Rama's kingdom, but did not know that he was their father!

As the years passed, Luv and Kush grew up into smart boys under the love and care of their mother, Sita. They were also fortunate to receive the able guidance of Sage Valmiki.

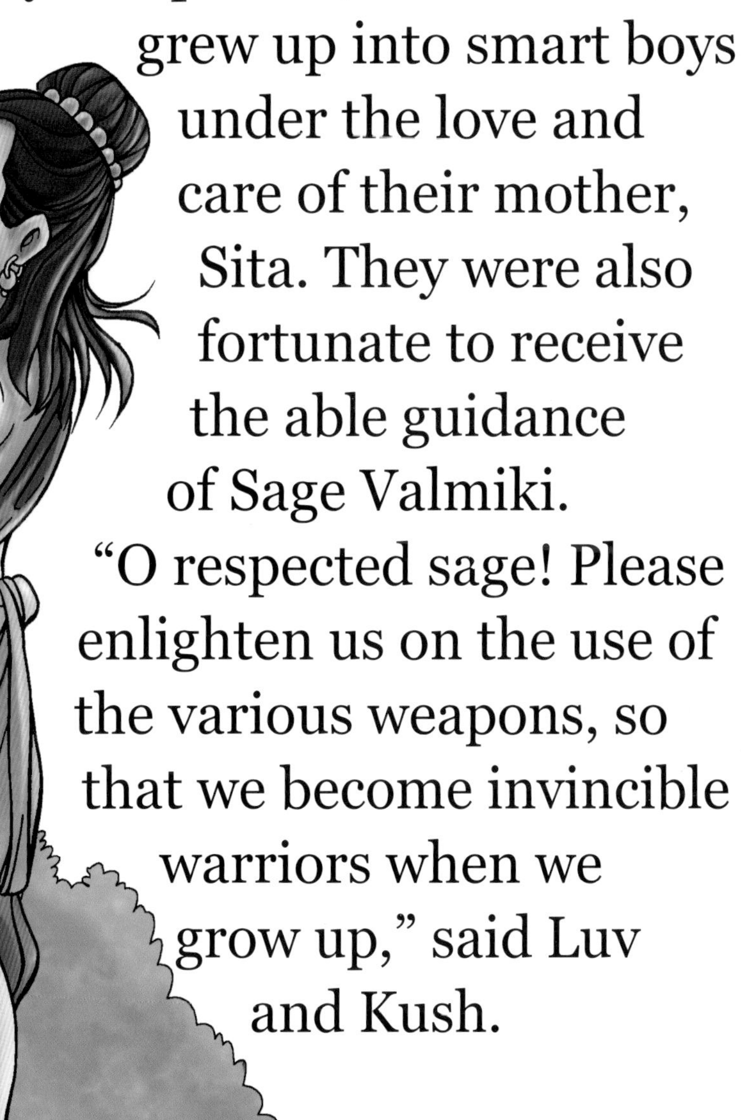

"O respected sage! Please enlighten us on the use of the various weapons, so that we become invincible warriors when we grow up," said Luv and Kush.

Sage Valmiki taught Luv and Kush the Vedas and the other religious texts. He also trained them in the usage of weapons. "Now, my boys, you have gained knowledge of all the decisive weapons!"

Meanwhile, in Ayodhya, Lord Rama thought of establishing his sovereignty. Sage Agastya advised him to perform the Ashwamedha-yajna. “Get a horse of white colour, and after worshipping it on Vaishakh Purnima, leave it to wander freely throughout the land.”

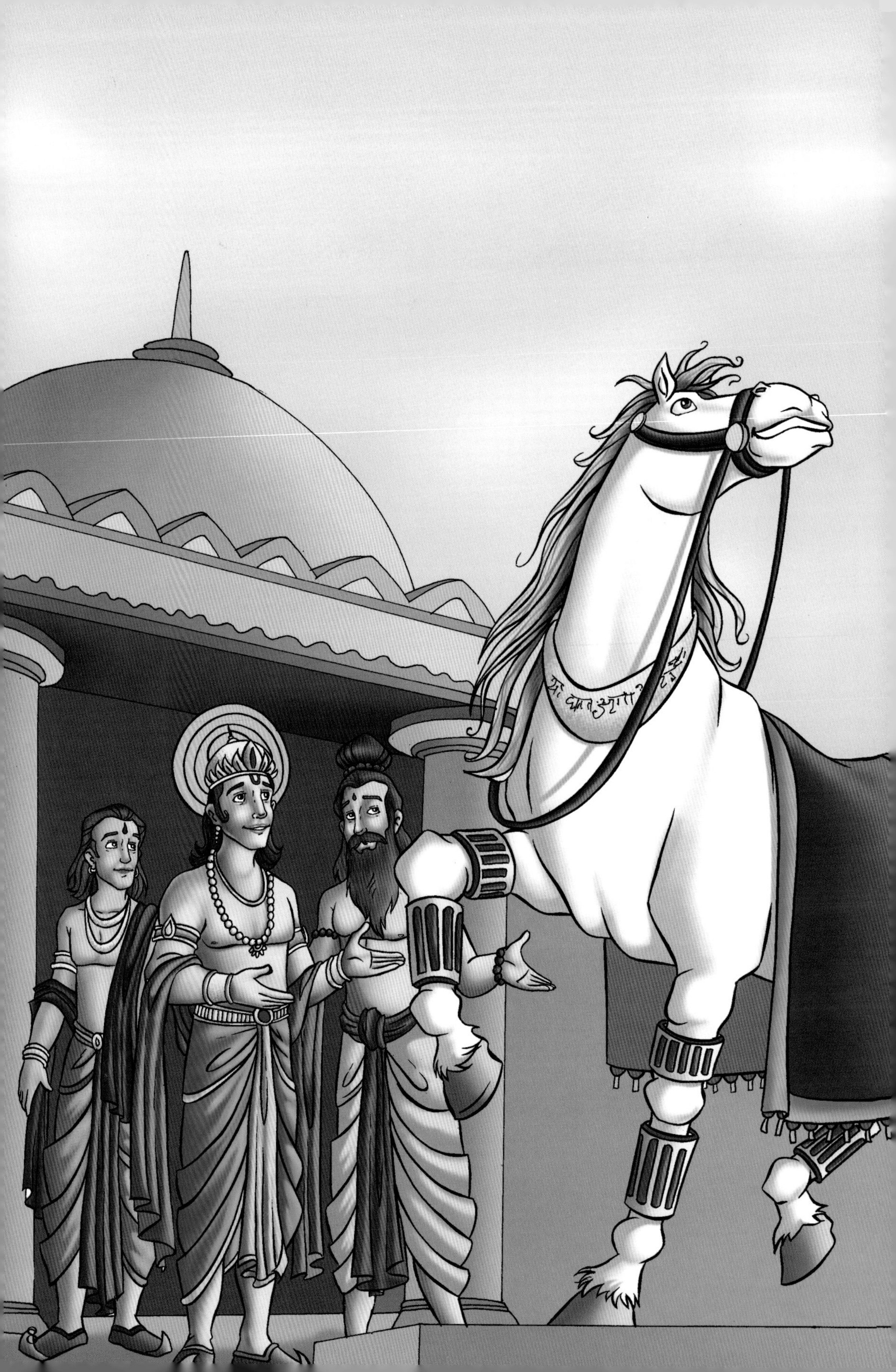

The day for the Ashwamedha-yajna finally arrived. A white horse was procured, bathed and beautifully decorated. A gold plate was tied around its neck, inscribed with a message that said, 'Accept Lord Rama as the Emperor, and leave the horse to roam around the world.' The message also included a warning that anyone who dared to hold the horse in captivity, would be severely dealt with.

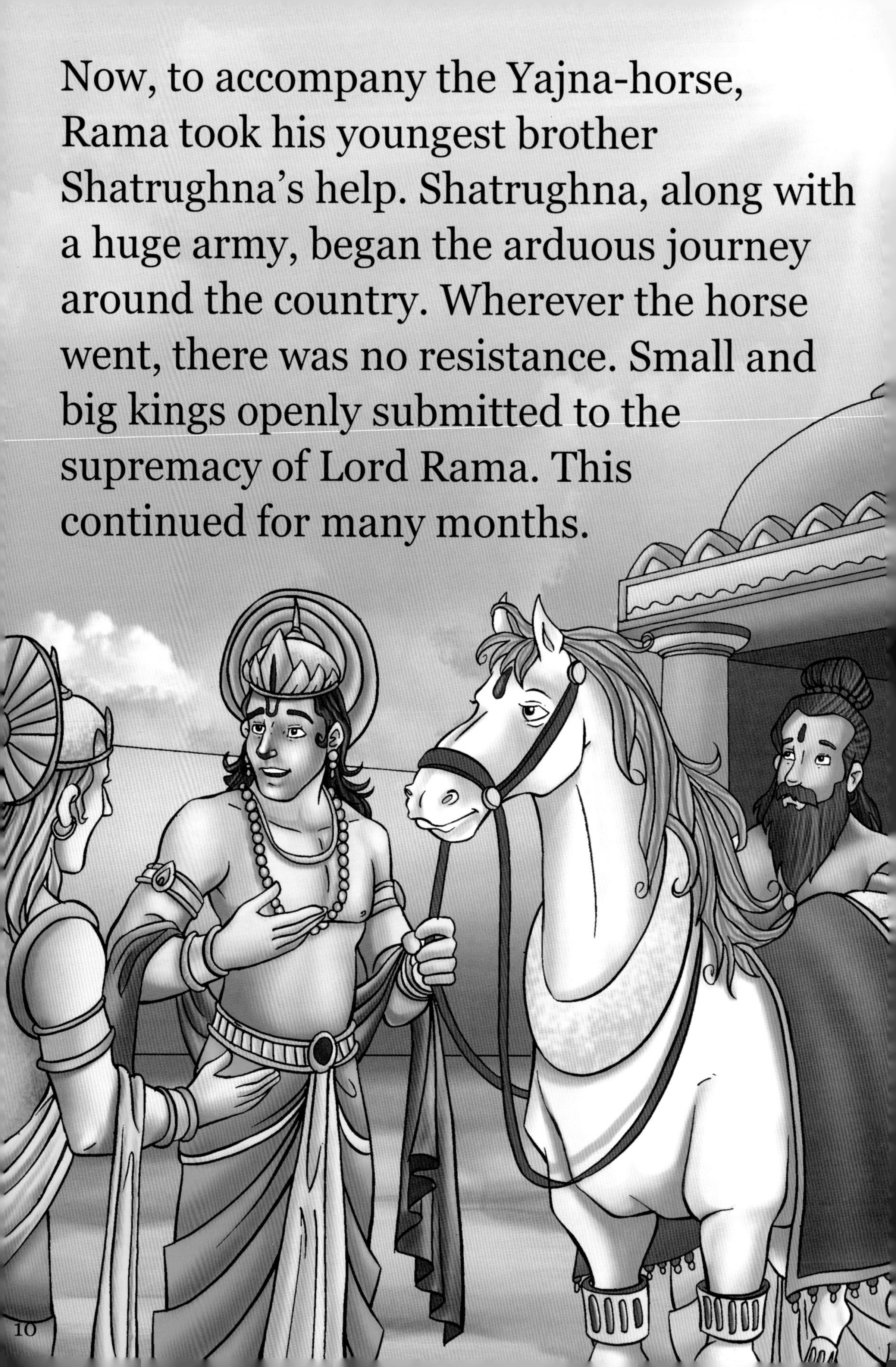

Now, to accompany the Yajna-horse, Rama took his youngest brother Shatrughna's help. Shatrughna, along with a huge army, began the arduous journey around the country. Wherever the horse went, there was no resistance. Small and big kings openly submitted to the supremacy of Lord Rama. This continued for many months.

One day, when Luv and Kush were busy playing in the forest after their lessons, they saw a beautiful white horse. It was the same Yajna-horse. "Luv, isn't the horse lovely? Let's take it to mother," said Kush, ecstatically. Not knowing anything about the Ashwamedha sacrifice, they captured the horse, and led it to their mother.

When they reached the ashram (hermitage), everyone was astounded. "What have you done, my dear? This is a Yajna-horse. Release it at once," said their mother, nervously. But, Luv-Kush refused to do so, saying, "Don't worry mother. If anybody comes to take the horse back, they will have to fight us!

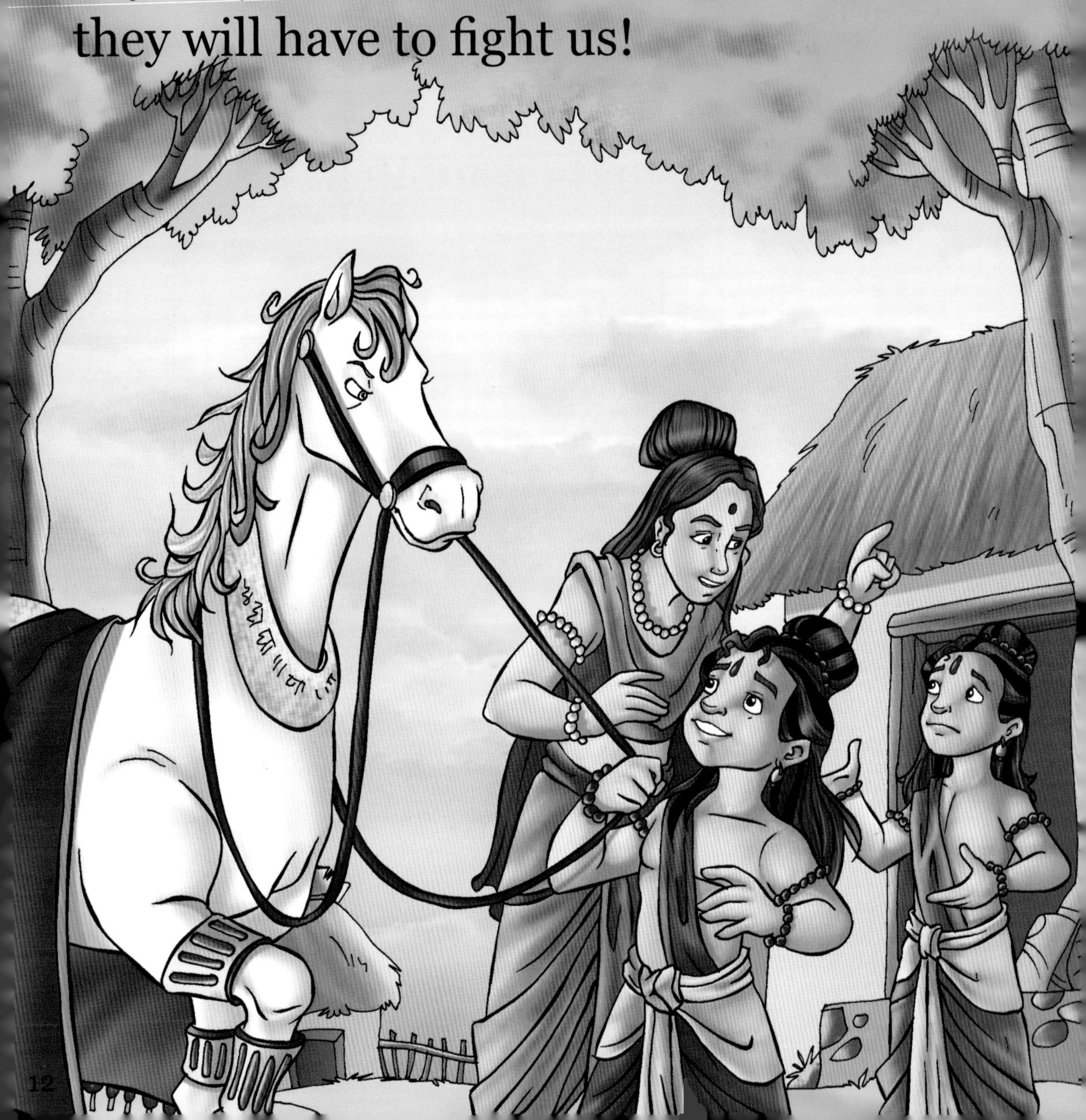

When Shatrughna realized that the yajna-horse had been captured, he was curious to know about the doer of this daring deed. Following the horse with his army, Shatrughna reached Valmiki's ashram.

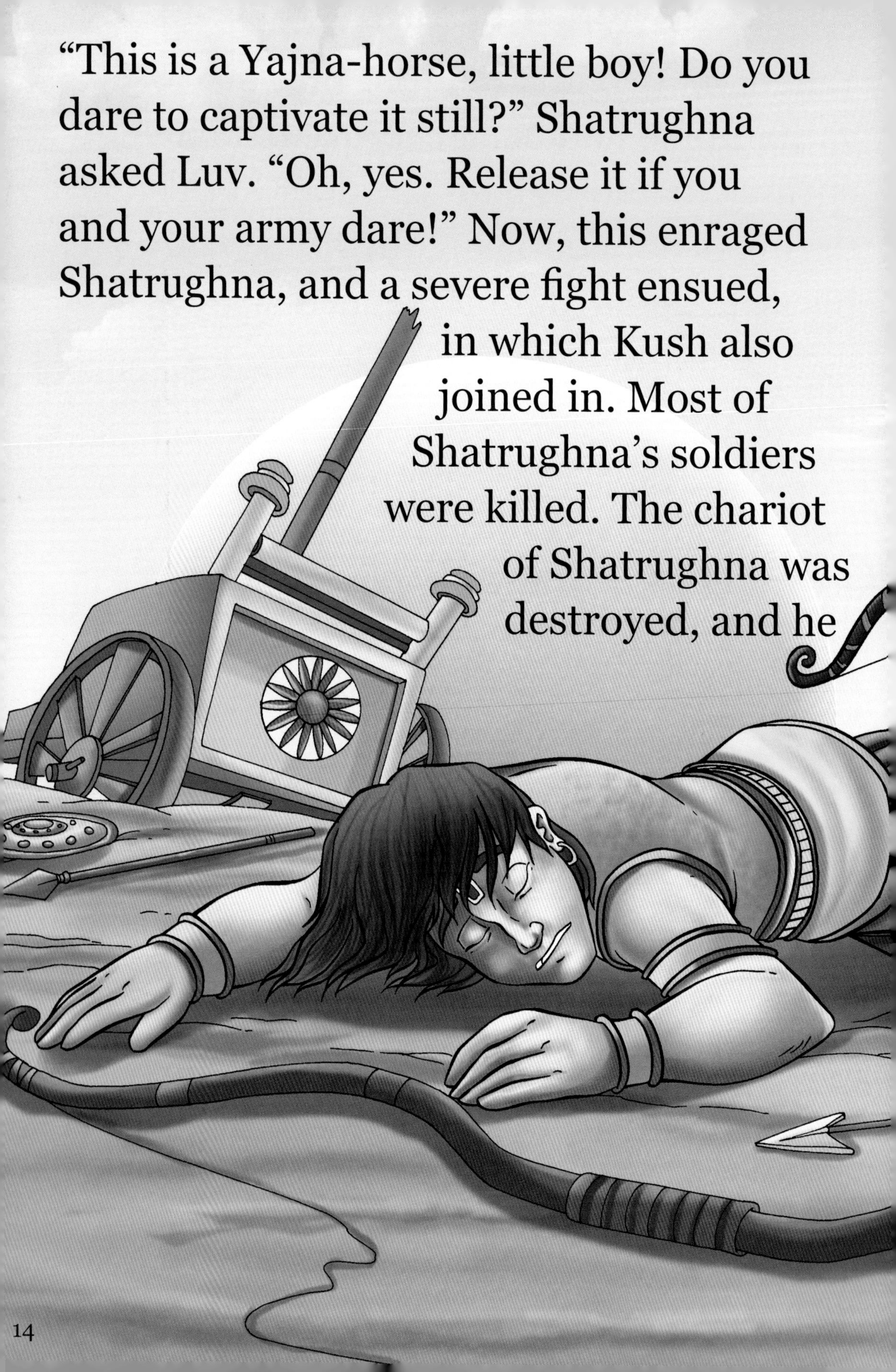

“This is a Yajna-horse, little boy! Do you dare to captivate it still?” Shatrughna asked Luv. “Oh, yes. Release it if you and your army dare!” Now, this enraged Shatrughna, and a severe fight ensued, in which Kush also joined in. Most of Shatrughna’s soldiers were killed. The chariot of Shatrughna was destroyed, and he

himself was seriously wounded. ‘I wonder who these children are! They do not seem to be any Rishi’s sons,’ he thought, before he fell down, unconscious.

When the news of the capture of the yajna-horse reached Ayodhya, Lakshmana immediately took charge of the army, and proceeded to fight Luv and Kush. He was surprised when he reached the battlefield. Most of the soldiers and his brother, Shatrughna, were lying on the ground, wounded. "Poor brother Shatrughna! Who is responsible for your miserable condition?" he asked, worriedly.

When Lakshmana stood wondering what to do next, his eyes fell on the little heroes, Luv and Kush. "Are you both responsible for my brother's agony?"

"Yes. Anybody who wishes to take back the yajna-horse will have to fight us." Awestruck, Lakshmana had no other option, but to fight with the little heroes. A fierce fight ensued, in which Luv and Kush nearly killed the whole army. At last, Kush sent the Brahmasthra towards Lakshmana. Unable to bear the power of the invincible weapon, Lakshmana fell down, unconscious.

The devastating news of Lakshmana's fall reached Ayodhya in no time. Lord Rama, with the aid of his younger brother, Bharata, and his ardent devotee, Hanuman, proceeded to Valmiki's hermitage to fight Luv and Kush. On reaching the hermitage, the army of monkeys, under the leadership of Hanuman, uprooted big trees and used them as weapons against the boys. But Luv, with a single arrow, routed the entire army. Bharata too fell down, unconscious.

Until this time, Lord Rama had not joined in the battle. But now he came near Luv and Kush. "Who are you, little heroes? Who is your father? I cannot fight you until you reveal your lineage," said Lord Rama, lovingly. "We are the sons of mother Sita, daughter of King Janak. We live in Sage Valmiki's hermitage. He is our teacher, and has aided us in gaining knowledge of the weapons."

This little piece of information was sufficient to make Lord Rama ecstatic. The little heroes were bent upon fighting with Lord Rama, but he was so engrossed in their charm and glory that he never cared to shoot an arrow at them. The twins kept on shooting a volley of arrows at Lord Rama, but he diverted them with ease. All the while, his heart swelled with fatherly pride at his sons' bravery.

Hanuman, who was watching all this patiently, was puzzled and outraged by the attempt of the young warriors on Lord Rama. He jumped into the arena with his mace to help his master. "Jai Shree Rama! You little warriors, how can you harm my master when I am present?"

However, Hanuman was soon spellbound to see the courage and skill of the young boys. After a long battle, Hanuman gave up, and Kush bound him with a rope. After a while, with Hanuman and the Yajna-horse, Luv and Kush approached their mother, Sita.

Bowing before her, they offered the booty acquired as homage to her. “Mother, see what we have achieved!” said the little boys, swelling in pride.

Sita was amazed at the sight of Hanuman bound so helplessly. "What have you done, children? Release him at once!" "But mother, he was fighting us with a mace," said Luv, in a complaining tone. Meanwhile, Hanuman was overjoyed to see Sita alive, and bowed down at her feet.

Just then, Sage Valmiki reached the hermitage. He gave an account of all that had happened to Sita who was very astonished. Valmiki released Hanuman and the Yajna-horse, and cried out, "Boys! What have you done? You have come here after felling Lakshmana, Bharata and Shatrughna!" Hearing this, Sita was speechless with fear and sorrow.

Seeing the agony of Sita, Sage Valmiki consoled her and tried to instil some courage in her. “Don’t worry, dear child. The time is ripe now when everything will end in your well being. Then, accompanied by Kush and Luv, he went with Sita to the battlefield.

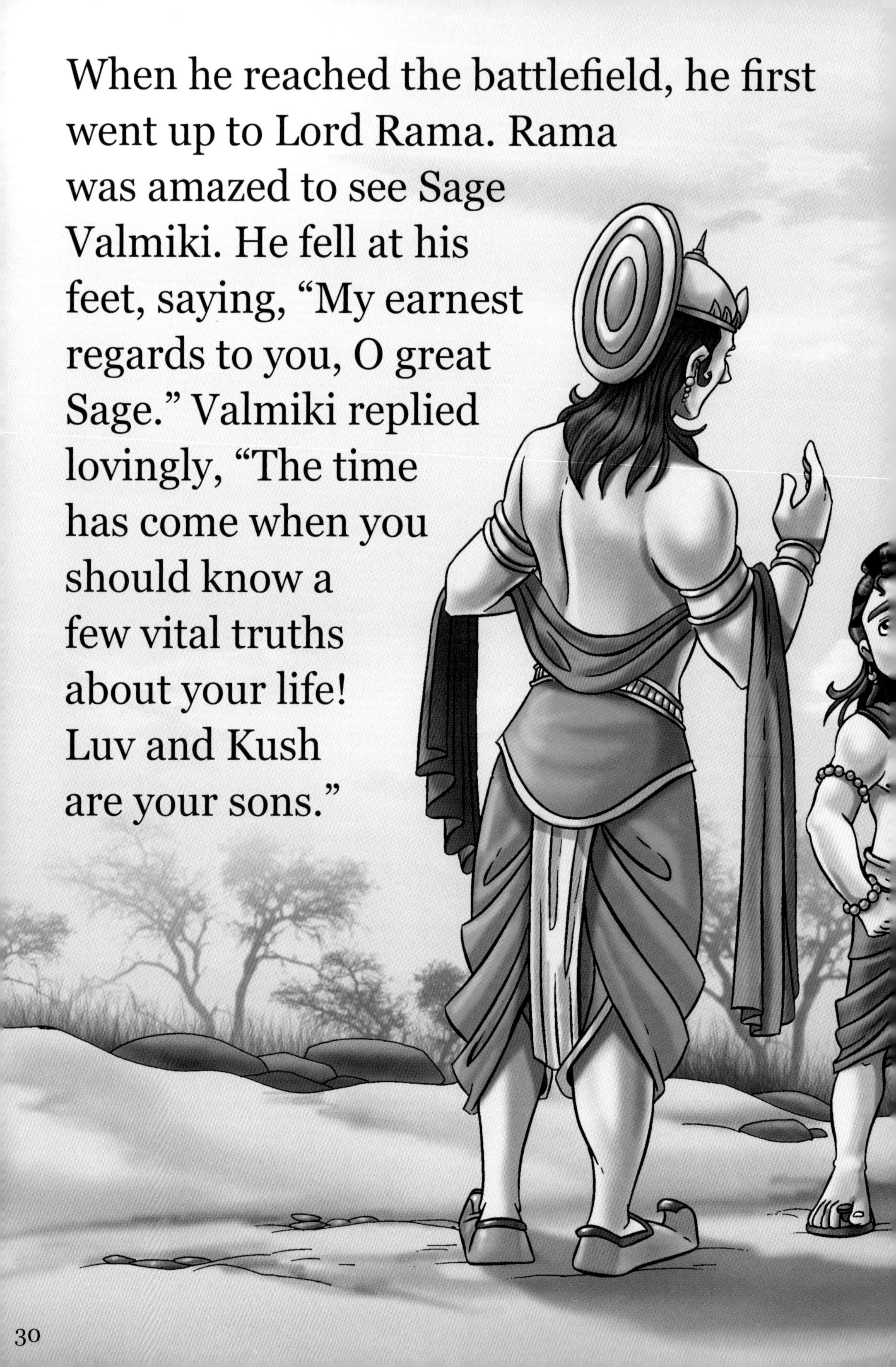

When he reached the battlefield, he first went up to Lord Rama. Rama was amazed to see Sage Valmiki. He fell at his feet, saying, “My earnest regards to you, O great Sage.” Valmiki replied lovingly, “The time has come when you should know a few vital truths about your life! Luv and Kush are your sons.”

Then, he described how Sita lived in his hermitage, where Kush and Luv were born. “May this universe be my witness.”

Lord Rama lovingly embraced his two sons.

Sage Valmiki showered magical nectar over the dead army, and all the dead soldiers became alive once again! Shatrughna, Bharata and Lakshmana regained their consciousness too. Luv and Kush accompanied their father, Rama to Ayodhya to become the lawful heirs to the throne of their kingdom.